TAM'S JOURNEY - The Middle

by Amanda Peddle

Illustrated by Rowan Ellis, Connor Lee and Abigail McArthur

Graphic Design, Layout and Editing - Mark Sosbe

Printing and Editing Support - Jenwoods Printers

TAM Publishing

First Published in Great Britain in 2020 by TAM Publishing

ISBN: 978-1-9160340-1-3

Printed in United Kingdom

Tam Publishing, Part of Inside Out OSYP (Outreach Services For Young People)

Minster on Sea, Sheerness, Kent, ME12 2GE.

www.insideoutosyp.co.uk

Taking Hetty's advice, Tam had drawn his own caveman at home and made a list of the things that he reacted to. By doing this, Tam could recognise things that made him 'feel'.

What was still happening, though, was whenever Tam had one of those feelings, he got a really strange gurgling in his tummy and his face went very, very red.

Sometimes, when he was really cross, his legs felt all wobbly as if they had turned into jelly!

It was most annoying, and Tam would feel very embarrassed and confused.

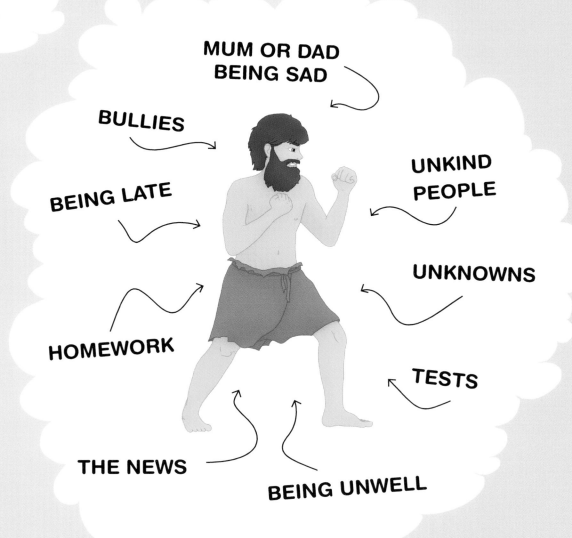

MUM OR DAD
BEING SAD

BULLIES

UNKIND
PEOPLE

BEING LATE

UNKNOWNS

HOMEWORK

TESTS

THE NEWS

BEING UNWELL

So, Tam decided that he would walk into the forest to visit his friend Hetty, to see if she could help him.

This time, he was more sensible about his journey and made sure to take a drink and a snack with him when he went.

Tam remembered the way much more clearly than before, now that he was walking and concentrating on where he was going, rather than running in a temper.

He realised how very beautiful the walk was. The trees were blossoming, and the birds were singing cheerfully.

The walk made him feel very calm and relaxed.

Soon, Tam arrived at the spot where he had met Hetty before.

He couldn't see Hetty around but soon remembered that, because she was a Sloth, it took a little while for her to move through the trees.

So, he took off his bag, sat down at the foot of an enormous tree and quietly enjoyed his snack of a tasty gingerbread man.

After a while, Tam heard a rustling noise, and sure enough, very slowly, he saw Hetty making her way down the tree towards him.

"I had wondered if that was you!" Hetty exclaimed. *"It is very, very good to see you again, Tam. How have you been?"*

"Hello Hetty!" said Tam. "I've had a very good week. I don't feel quite so sad now that I understand what my brain is trying to do."

"That's fantastic news!" Hetty said with a warm smile on her face. "Anything that can make us understand our bodies better is a good thing!"

"Yes, definitely!" said Tam. "In fact, I came to ask if you would be able to help me with something; a feeling that I don't quite understand."

"Of course! What is it you would like help with?" Hetty asked.

14.

"Well," said Tam, *"I have noticed that when I feel a feeling that is not that helpful, my body feels strange; in all different places. I have never noticed it before, but now that I am thinking more clearly, I seem to notice it a lot."*

"Ah, I know what you're talking about," Hetty said confidently, *"and I can explain that quite easily."*

She slowly stretched out her arm towards the ground, picked up a twig and started to draw in the dirt.

Tam watched as an outline began to take shape. It looked like a gingerbread man, like the ones he'd brought to snack on!

Tam wondered how Hetty knew what a gingerbread man looked like. Maybe she had had one before? Do sloths like gingerbread men? Did she see him eating his when she was climbing down? He didn't know, but one thing he did know was that she was full of surprises!

Hetty finally finished drawing and looked up at Tam.

"When your brain and body react to the safe threats that we talked about, they send messages around the body in the form of chemicals and hormones.

"These physical signs can tell us a lot; they can also be like clues to give you some warning if your body is trying to react to a situation that won't cause you harm."

Hetty went back to her gingerbread shape and drew a heart and some lungs.

"To start with, your heart beats faster to send blood to the muscles, and you start to breathe deeper for oxygen. This is called the 'fight, flight or freeze response' because your body is getting ready for action. You might notice your heart pumping hard, like a beating in your chest. Sometimes, you can feel as if you're breathing too fast, which can make you a little dizzy."

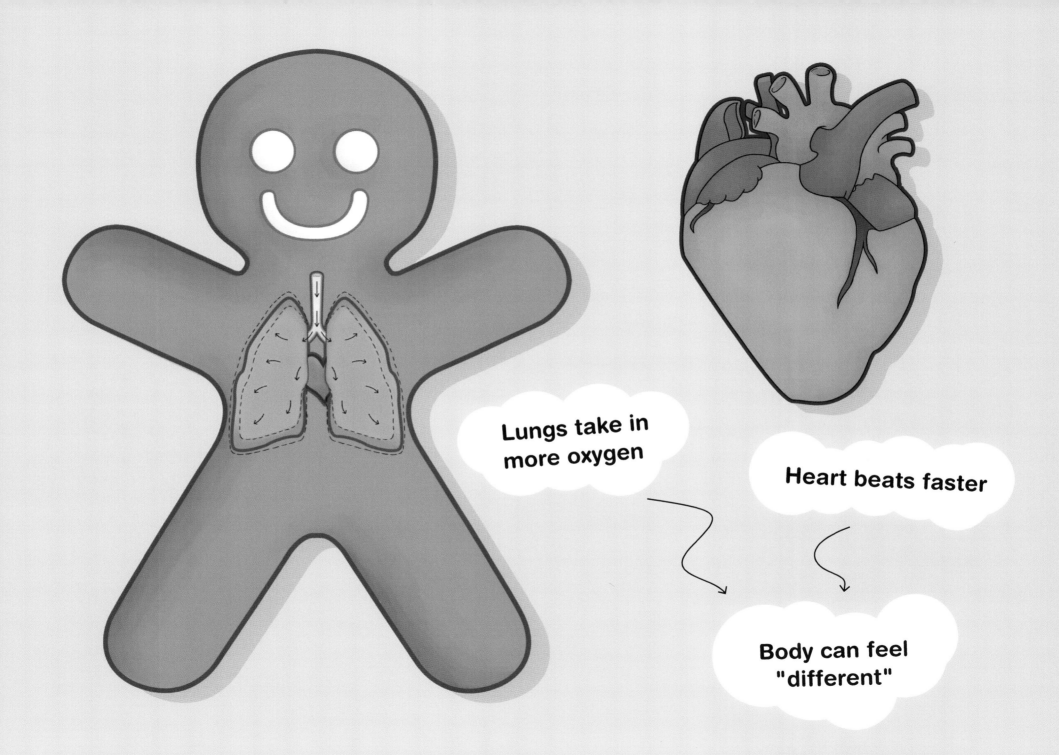

"Your tummy, for example", said Hetty, drawing a tummy.

"The reason it feels funny is because the oxygen you breathe in increases when you get worried or cross, so you end up having too much of it.

"It races around and around the body in your blood and it changes the 'feel' of things.

"Your tummy reacts to that, so, it has a little 'flutter'; sometimes that can feel like a pain, or butterflies flying around in your tummy, or a funny wobbly feeling."

SOME OF THE THINGS OUR TUMMIES CAN MAKE US FEEL

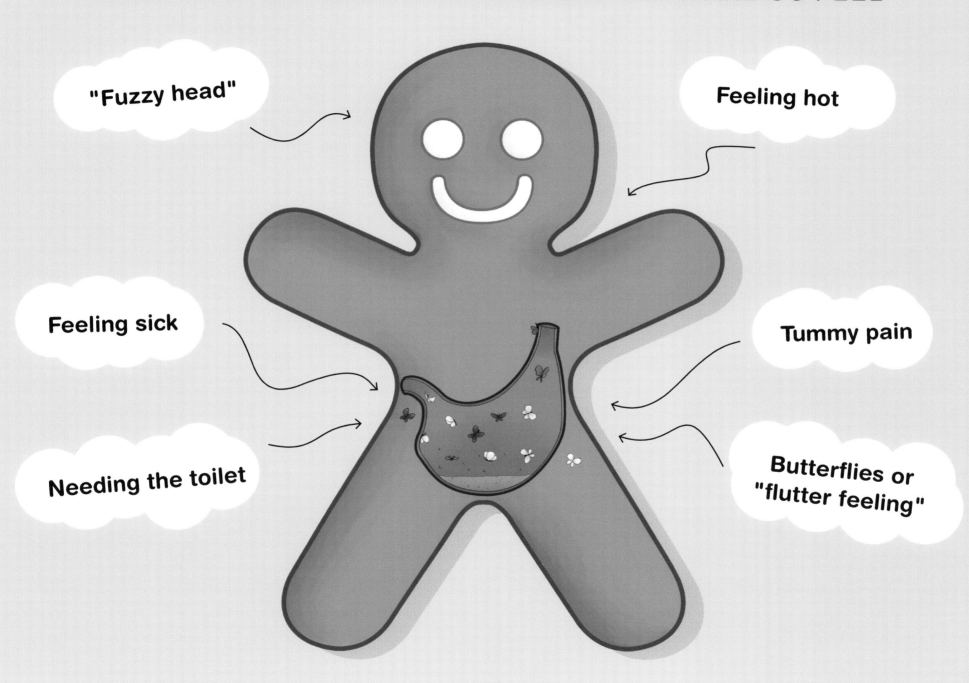

Tam was amazed; not only did he have a unique brain, he now had all sorts of things racing around inside him doing all sorts of clever things.

Hetty looked at Tam's face and smiled. *"It's a lot to remember Tam,"* she said, *"but there are lots of parts of the body that can be affected, as well as the tummy."*

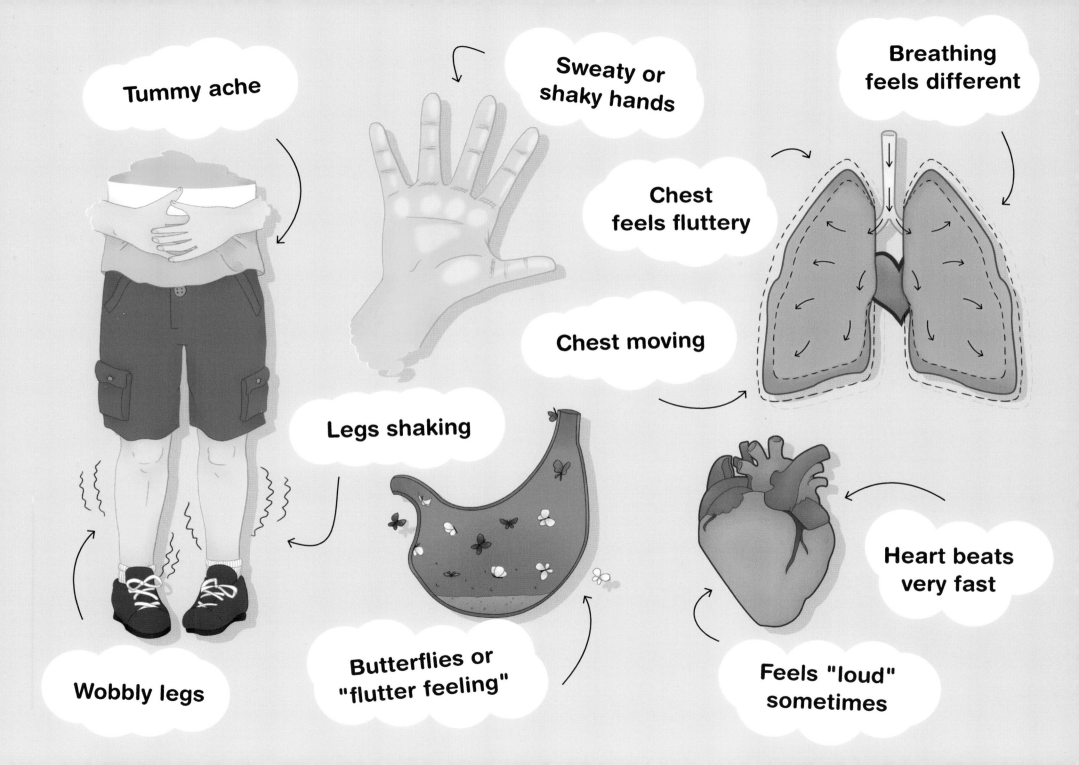

"It's all designed to help you become 'alert' to keep you safe. Of course, nowadays you aren't really at risk from a lot of the things that cause a reaction," said Hetty.

"It's just that your brain is very, very busy and sometimes tries to keep you safe when you're not in any danger, so instead you have this feeling that's uncomfortable.

"If your brain and body can't decide what to do sometimes, if you 'freeze' or stay 'alert' for too long, you can get too full of oxygen.

"Tam, do you remember when we talked about the 'fight, flight or freeze response' in the brain?" asked Hetty with a kind smile. *"It's very important, and those physical 'feels' are just there to tell you when that response may be happening."*

FIGHT
ATTACK THE DANGER
& DEFEND YOURSELF

FLIGHT
RUN AWAY FROM
DANGER

FREEZE MEANS WE
CAN'T DECIDE

"*Goodness,*" said Tam. "*That does explain my funny tummy feeling and my red face.*

"*So, it's not anything to be scared of, Hetty? It does feel quite uncomfortable sometimes.*"

"*No, Tam,*" said Hetty in a comforting voice. "*It's nothing to be scared or worried about, but it does help for you to know what it is and that can help you to feel calmer and less worried.*"

Tam felt so much better and a little surprised. He knew his brain was clever, but now that he knew even more about how it talked to his body, he was feeling very amazed.

"*Thank you for explaining it all to me, Hetty!*" said Tam with a wide grin. "*Would you like to share my gingerbread men?*"

"*Yes please, Tam,*" replied Hetty with a smile. "*I would like that very much.*"

Hetty looked up at Tam and realised it was starting to get dark.

"That's enough for one day, Tam. You had better get home before it gets too late," she said.

Hetty looked thoughtful for a moment, *"Why don't you have a think about your body, and maybe draw your own gingerbread man to show me next time?"*

"That's a good idea, Hetty! I will do that!" replied Tam, excited at the thought of visiting his friend again.

"Then, when you come back," said Hetty, *"I can explain more about how we can help ourselves a little when we feel this way. Most importantly, though, remember: this is your body's way of being, and it does not make you unusual.*

"Everyone has these 'feels', and everyone's are slightly different.

"And that," said Hetty with a smile, *"is OK."*

A word from Amanda:

The main reason that I chose the sloth as the character for Hetty was the science behind their evolution.
Like us, sometimes, sloths are one of the most misunderstood creatures on the planet. While they look slow and comical, they are actually an evolutionary masterpiece, and they have developed some of the most important systems in order to be one of our most long evolving Earth inhabitants.

I am delighted that Dr Rebecca Cliffe, from The Sloth Conservation Foundation, is sharing some of the science with us in the book.

Dr Rebecca Cliffe, The Sloth Conservation Foundation

"Sloths have evolved to be the planet's slowest mammals – but why are they so slow? And why does it work? There are several factors that contribute to the sloths slow pace, the first one is surprisingly simple: sloths can't see very well! Scientists think that the sloths we see today may have evolved from a creature that lived underground 64 million years ago. At this stage in their evolution, sloths lost almost 90% of their vision (because living underground means that you don't really need to be able to see very well). Throughout their evolutionary history sloths never re-gained the ability to see, and so when they finally became tree-dwelling animals they had no choice but to move slowly (if you can't see very well and you try to run around in the trees then you are going to fall out). By moving slowly and carefully the sloths were able to thrive in the canopy!